The Fox Primary School

Kensington Place
London W8 7PP
Tel: 020 7727 7637
Fax: 020 7229 4628

What is phonics?

Phonics helps children learn to read and write by teaching them the letter sounds (known as phonemes), rather than the letter names, e.g. the sound that 'c' makes rather than its alphabetic name. They then learn how to blend the sounds: the process of saying the sounds in a word or 'sounding out' and then blending them together to make the word, for example c – a – t = cat. Once the phonemes and the skill of blending are learnt, children can tackle reading any phonetically decodable word they come across, even ones they don't know, with confidence and success.

However, there are of course many words in the English language that aren't phonetically decodable, e.g. if a child gets stuck on 'the' it doesn't help if they sound it out and blend it. We call these 'tricky words' and they are just taught as words that are so 'tricky' that children have to learn to recognise them by sight.

How do phonic readers work?

Phonic reading books are written especially for children who are beginning to learn phonics at nursery or school, and support any programme being used by providing plenty of practice as children develop the skills of decoding and blending. By targeting specific phonemes and tricky words, increasing in difficulty, they ensure systematic progression with reading.

Because phonic readers are primarily decodable – aside from the target tricky words which need to be learnt, children should be able to read the books with real assurance and accomplishment.

Big Cat phonic readers:
A Day Out

In Big Cat phonic readers the specific phonemes and tricky words being focussed on are highlighted here in these notes, so that you can be clear about what your child's learning and what they need to practise.

While reading at home together, there are all sorts of fun additional games you can play to help your child practise those phonemes and tricky words, which can be a nice way to familiarise yourselves with them before reading, or remind you of them after you've finished. In *A Day Out*, for example:

- the focus phonemes are ir (bird), ow (window), y (fly), ea (reach). Why not write them down and encourage your child to practise saying the sounds as you point to them in a random order. This is called 'Speed Sounds' and as you get faster and faster with your pointing, it encourages your child to say them as quickly as possible. You can try reversing the roles, so that you have a practice too!

- the tricky words are 'two' and 'like'. You can play 'Hide and Seek' by asking your child to close their eyes and count to 10, while you write each word on a piece of paper, hiding them somewhere in the room you're in or the garden for your child to find. As they find each one, they should try reading and spelling the word out.

Reading together

- Have a look at the front cover of *A Day Out* and talk about what you can see.

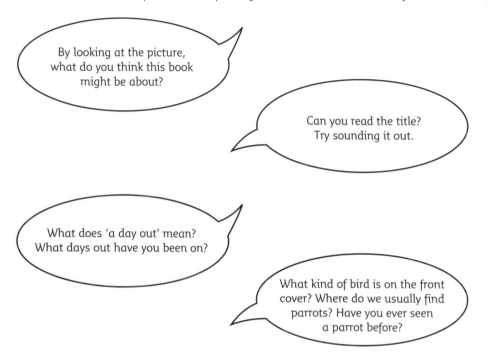

By looking at the picture, what do you think this book might be about?

Can you read the title? Try sounding it out.

What does 'a day out' mean? What days out have you been on?

What kind of bird is on the front cover? Where do we usually find parrots? Have you ever seen a parrot before?

- Enjoy reading *A Day Out* together, noticing the focus phonemes (ir, ow, y, ea) and tricky words (two, like). It's useful to point to each word as your child reads, and encouraging to give them lots of praise as they go.

- If your child gets stuck on a word, and it's phonetically decodable, encourage them to sound it out. You can practise blending by saying the sounds aloud a few times, getting quicker and quicker. If they still can't read it, tell them the word and move on.

Talking about the book

- Use the story map on pp18–19 to retell the story together, in the right order, and talk about the dangers the parrot faced.

- Practise the focus phonemes from *A Day Out* by asking your child to find specific words with, for example, the 'ow' phoneme, or sounding out some of the key words.

A Day Out

Written and illustrated by
Petr Horáček

Collins

The granny is sleeping.
The cat is looking at the bird.
Look! The bird can get out!
It is time for the bird to fly.

The cat jumps up. The bird
jumps off his perch. Look out!
He flies out into the room.
He must get away.

The bird flies out of the
window, out of the room, out
of the house. Just in time.
The bird is out. The bird is free.

It is windy, but the sun is out.
It is fun to fly. But look out ...
What is it? It is a dog.
A big dog!

The bird hides in the bird stand.
He likes it in there. It is safe,
no one can get him in
the bird stand.

But look out! The dog can see
the bird. The bird stand is too
small for the two of them.
The bird flies out. Just in time.

The bird flies past the farm.
But wait ... Look! A fox is lying
in the bush. The fox is looking
at the bird.

The fox runs after the bird,
but it is too slow. He cannot
reach the fast bird. The bird
flies to the wood. Just in time.

13

It is a deep, dark wood.
But wait ... Look out!
A stag is standing by the tree.
It is time to fly home.

The bird flies out of the wood,
past the farm, into the garden
and into the house. The granny
is waiting there.

The bird is back home.
Just in time. He flies in and
sits on the perch. There is
no stag, no fox, no dog, no cat.
It is safe.

16

The granny is looking
at the bird. She shuts him
safe inside. The bird likes her.
It is good to be home.

Bird's day out

Getting creative

- Have some fun with your child by playing a simple ball game to practise the phonemes, where you write the focus phonemes on pieces of paper, spread them out on the floor at one end of the room and ask your child to roll the ball at one of the phonemes – saying the sound if they land on it.

- You could practise the tricky words by encouraging your child to spell out the word as they bounce the ball to you. This can be repeated lots of times!

- If your child's enjoyed reading *A Day Out*, they could choose a pet and create a poster with a picture of it and some simple instructions all about how to look after it.

Other books at Level 2:

Fiction	Non-fiction
Zog and Zebra Mal Peet and Elspeth Graham Sarah Horne	**The Sun and the Moon** Paul Shipton
The Singing Beetle Linda Strachan · Oliver Hurst	**The Rainforest at Night** Nic Bishop
A Day Out Petr Horáček	**Gorillas** Teresa Heapy

Collins Big Cat
Reading Lions

Published by Collins
An imprint of HarperCollins*Publishers*
1 London Bridge Street
London
SE1 9GF

© HarperCollins*Publishers* Limited 2013
This edition was published in 2015.

Author and illustrator: Petr Horáček

Petr Horáček asserts his moral right to be identified as the author of this work.

British Library Cataloguing in Publication Data
A catalogue record for this publication is available from the British Library.

Designer: Anna Stasinska, anna@annaStasinska.demon.co.uk
Parent notes authors: Sue Reed and Liz Webster

Printed and bound by RR Donnelley APS

www.collins.co.uk/parents